A THINK AND WRITE BOOK

THE WRITER'S TOOLBOX

EDUCATIONAL DESIGN, INC.   **EDI 276**

Table of Contents

Introduction

What makes a good writer?

Obviously, many things. But good writers have a lot in common, even when they have different writing styles and are writing about different things. Good writers use words well. They write vividly, with detail and with fresh use of language. Their sentences are varied. Their paragraphs are well constructed and well developed.

This book, *The Writer's Toolbox*, will show you how to use some of the tools of the good writer. You will start off by learning some ways to find the "right" words that will reflect what you are trying to say. You will learn how to vary your sentences and make them more complex, and how to avoid common mistakes in sentence construction. Finally, you will learn how to put your sentences together into paragraphs that express your thoughts well and that are clear, unified, and smoothly written.

CHOOSING THE BEST WORD

1. General and Specific Writing

Good writing should be specific, not general. If people tell you to "be more specific" when you speak or write, they are telling you to use more detail or be more exact in your choice of words. "Specific" is the opposite of "general." General means NOT detailed or exact.

Nouns are words that name persons, places, or things. A general noun names a large group. A specific noun names a smaller group. "Animal" is a more general noun than "dog" because "animal" refers to a larger group. Any kind of animal could be in that group, not only dogs.

Is "dog" a general or a specific word? It is not possible to answer this question unless we know what other word "dog" is being compared to. "Dog" is more general than "collie" or "German shepherd" but more specific than "animal" or "pet."

One way to make your writing more specific is to use proper nouns rather than common nouns. A proper noun names one specific person, place, or thing. Harriet Tubman was a specific person. Boston is a specific city. Proper nouns are always capitalized.

Another way to make writing more specific is to add adjectives (words and phrases that tell what kind, which one, or how many) to the nouns you have chosen. "A house burned down" is not as specific as "The SPOOKY GRAY house ACROSS THE STREET burned down."

Below each question, check the letter that answers the question correctly.

1. Which of these nouns is the most general because it includes the most things?

    _____ (A) food
    _____ (B) fruit
    _____ (C) vegetable

2. Which of these nouns is the most specific because it includes the fewest things?

    _____ (A) vehicle
    _____ (B) dump truck
    _____ (C) truck

3. Which of these nouns is the most general because it includes the most things?

    _____ (A) pajamas
    _____ (B) nightgown
    _____ (C) flannel nightie

4. Which of these nouns is the most specific because it includes the fewest things?

    _____ (A) stories
    _____ (B) reading material
    _____ (C) mystery stories

For each pair of nouns below, write G if the first word is more general than the second.
Write S if the first word is the more specific of the two.

5.	building	church	_____
6.	collie	dog	_____
7.	pizza	food	_____
8.	boy	Charles	_____
9.	clothing	shirt	_____
10.	almond	nut	_____
11.	book	dictionary	_____
12.	checkers	game	_____

In the blank space, write the more specific word(s) in each of the following pairs.

13. skyscraper   building   _____

14. skyscraper   Empire State Building   _____

15. vegetable   carrot   _____

16. vegetable   food   _____

17. man   person   _____

18. man   Mr. Cummings   _____

19. furniture   bedroom dresser   _____

In the blank, write the letter of the most specific choice.

20. My little brother always eats _____ for breakfast.

    (A) cereal
    (B) something
    (C) Cheerios

21. When we visited New York, we saw _____ .

    (A) the Empire State Building
    (B) a tall building
    (C) a skyscraper

22.	Yesterday _____ went shopping all afternoon.

    (A) the two girls
    (B) Jennifer and Katie
    (C) they

23.	Sharon, Joan, and I played _____ together after school yesterday.

    (A) a board game
    (B) a game
    (C) Monopoly

24.	I've already grown out of the _____ I wore last year.

    (A) ski jacket
    (B) clothes
    (C) winter coat

Underline the adjectives or adjective phrases in the following sentences.

25.	The angry woman shouted at me.

26.	The boy in the corner started to giggle.

27.	Two red cars raced down the street.

28.	The dusty book was lying on the table in the hallway.

29.	I enjoy reading mystery stories on a rainy day.

30.	The telephone repairman was wearing a navy blue tee shirt.

Check the letter of the most specific word or phrase.

31.	_____	(A) short man
    _____	(B) person
    _____	(C) short, fat man
    _____	(D) short, fat man with gray hair
    _____	(E) man

32. _____ (A) blue Cadillac
    _____ (B) light blue car with a dented fender
    _____ (C) blue car
    _____ (D) light blue Cadillac with a dented fender
    _____ (E) car with a dented fender

33. _____ (A) a fuzzy kitten
    _____ (B) a cat
    _____ (C) a fuzzy white kitten under the table
    _____ (D) a kitten
    _____ (E) a fuzzy white kitten under the kitchen table

34. _____ (A) a pad of yellow paper
    _____ (B) a pad of paper
    _____ (C) a pad of yellow lined paper
    _____ (D) paper
    _____ (E) a pad of yellow lined paper on the desk

Put the words or phrases in order, from most general to most specific.

EXAMPLE: (A) animal   **A C D B E**
         (B) German shepherd
         (C) mammal
         (D) dog
         (E) David's German shepherd

35. (A) steak   _____
    (B) overpriced sirloin steak
    (C) meat
    (D) sirloin steak
    (E) beefsteak

36. (A) pitcher for a major league team   _____
    (B) athlete
    (C) professional athlete
    (D) professional baseball player
    (E) pitcher for the New York Yankees

37. (A) my six-year-old nephew, Ralph   _____
    (B) boy
    (C) little boy
    (D) my six-year-old nephew
    (E) male

38. (A) cashews
    (B) food
    (C) roasted cashews in a bowl
    (D) nuts
    (E) roasted cashews

39. (A) motor vehicle
    (B) Datsun station wagon
    (C) vehicle
    (D) automobile
    (E) station wagon

40. (A) boa constrictor
    (B) reptile
    (C) animal
    (D) hungry boa constrictor
    (E) snake

41. (A) iris
    (B) purple Japanese iris
    (C) plant
    (D) flower
    (E) Japanese iris

42. (A) a cowardly lion
    (B) The Cowardly Lion
    (C) cat
    (D) mammal
    (E) lion

43. (A) an elderly woman
    (B) a person
    (C) a woman
    (D) a woman seventy years old
    (E) my seventy-year-old grandmother

44. (A) Sunday newspaper
    (B) sections of the Sunday newspaper
    (C) daily newspaper
    (D) newspaper
    (E) Sunday comics

12

45. (A) park
    (B) Pennsylvania's parks
    (C) vacation grounds
    (D) Ridley State Park in Chester County
    (E) state park

46. (A) long-sleeved shirt
    (B) plaid, button-down, long-sleeved shirt
    (C) clothing
    (D) shirt
    (E) button-down, long-sleeved shirt

47. (A) fruit tree
    (B) tree
    (C) apple tree
    (D) the Golden Delicious apple tree in the back yard
    (E) the apple tree in the back yard

2. General and Specific Verbs and Adverbs

Nouns such as "dog" and "Empire State Building" are not the only kinds of words which can be classified as general or specific. Verbs can also be general or specific. "Move" is more general than "run"; "run" is more general than "sprint."

One way of making general verbs more specific is to use adverbs. The phrase "walked slowly" is more specific than the word "walked." "Slowly," "quickly," and "carefully" are some of the adverbs which can be used to modify "walked." Many adverbs end in "-ly."

It is better to find a more specific verb than to use an adverb. There are many specific ways to say "walk": strut, march, stagger, stroll, saunter, pace, hike, amble, stride, parade, mince, hobble, and trudge are some examples. Each verb describes how someone walks.

The verb "say" is another common word which can often be replaced with more specific verbs such as: repeat, state, declare, remark, stutter, mutter, stammer, mention, grumble, comment, mumble. Each of these describes how a person says something.

In the blank, write the more specific word in each of the following pairs.

1.	chuckle	laugh	_____
2.	eat	gobble	_____
3.	rush	go	_____
4.	cry	whine	_____
5.	scribble	write	_____
6.	look	inspect	_____
7.	narrate	tell	_____
8.	slice	cut	_____
9.	clean	sweep	_____
10.	boil	cook	_____

Underline the adverb in each of the following sentences.

11. The teacher smiled cheerfully.

12. She slowly closed the heavy door.

13. We drove fast.

14. She accidentally broke her glasses.

15. Todd spoke loudly into the telephone.

16. She distinctly said, "Nine o'clock."

17. Wendy was especially excited about her birthday.

18. He moves quite slowly.

19. They playfully danced around the room.

20. He quietly sat in the corner.

Choose the word from those listed below each definition that most closely matches the definition. Use a dictionary if you need to.

21. to walk slowly, for pleasure _____

    (A) strut   (B) stride   (C) march   (D) stagger   (E) stroll

22. to walk with long steps _____

    (A) mince   (B) stride   (C) pace   (D) saunter   (E) amble

23. to walk in a proud way, as if showing off _____

    (A) hike   (B) stroll   (C) strut   (D) stride   (E) hobble

24. to say with great force _____

    (A) mutter   (B) comment   (C) reply   (D) declare   (E) stammer

25. to speak with pauses and repeated sounds _____

    (A) stammer   (B) repeat   (C) state   (D) comment   (E) mumble

15

26. to tell about in a few words   _____

    (A) stutter   (B) mention   (C) declare   (D) mumble   (E) comment

27. to cry very quietly   _____

    (A) howl   (B) squeal   (C) weep   (D) shout   (E) shriek

28. to eat something with very small bites   _____

    (A) devour   (B) nibble   (C) gulp   (D) gnaw   (E) crunch

29. to tap or hit something lightly   _____

    (A) tickle   (B) grasp   (C) hold   (D) grab   (E) pat

30. to go down or fall very slowly   _____

    (A) trip   (B) plunge   (C) dive   (D) sink   (E) tumble

Circle the adjectives and/or adverbs which make each sentence more specific.

31. The beach is a lonely, deserted place during the grey, chilly months of winter.

32. The fierce dog barked loudly at the passing cars.

33. Everyone gathered around the glowing fire to hear one of her frightening ghost stories.

34. I especially like hot, spicy foods.

35. The long, billowing kite lazily wafted against the clear blue sky.

36. Mark angrily kicked the greedy vending machine that had stolen his shiny new coins.

37. Janet and Lynn merrily made their way down the colorful, lively midway at the fair.

38. Three exhausted children trudged up the steep hill.

39. The faded, antique quilt, lovingly made by her grandmother, lay on her bed.

40. The talented carpenter carefully carved a delicate design into the small cabinet drawers.

41. His sopping, faded jeans hung from the drooping clothesline in the back yard.

42. She slipped her thick science report into the red plastic cover.

3. Shades of Meaning

A synonym is a word having the same, or almost the same, meaning as another word. Very few words are exact synonyms. "Saunter" and "stroll" mean almost exactly the same thing, but "stroll" and "pace" do not — even though all three words are different ways of saying "walk."

How can you decide exactly which specific word to use when you are writing? First you must know what you are trying to say; you must know in what *context* or setting the word will be used. The context of a written word is made up of all the words around it.

A dictionary is often not very helpful when you are trying to find synonyms or more specific words. A good book to use is a thesaurus (thi sôr'us). A thesaurus is a collection of synonyms, antonyms (opposites), and other words related by meaning. A thesaurus lists words but does not define or tell you how to pronounce them as a dictionary does.

Check the blank next to the letter which provides the correct answer.

1. A word that means almost the same as another word is called its:

    _____ (A) antonym.
    _____ (B) homonym.
    _____ (C) thesaurus.
    _____ (D) synonym.
    _____ (E) opposite.

2. Which pair of words includes synonyms?

    _____ (A) ask, inquire
    _____ (B) amble, stumble
    _____ (C) sprint, jog
    _____ (D) stroll, stride
    _____ (E) mention, declare

3. Which pair are not synonyms?

    _____ (A) reply, respond
    _____ (B) mutter, grumble
    _____ (C) rushed, hurried
    _____ (D) mumble, declare
    _____ (E) shout, yell

4. The context of a written word is:

    _____ (A) made up of other words around it.
    _____ (B) its denotation and connotation.
    _____ (C) more specific than general.
    _____ (D) usually found in a good thesaurus.
    _____ (E) more than one of the above.

5. A thesaurus is:

_____ (A) just like a dictionary.
_____ (B) a book of lists of words related by meaning.
_____ (C) a word meaning the same as another.
_____ (D) not helpful when you are writing.

6. You could use a thesaurus to:

_____ (A) learn how to pronounce "thesaurus."
_____ (B) look up a more specific way of writing "walked."
_____ (C) look up the meaning of "thesaurus."
_____ (D) do more than one of the above.

7. Two words are antonyms if they are:

_____ (A) opposites.
_____ (B) synonyms.
_____ (C) related.
_____ (D) in a thesaurus.
_____ (E) pronounced the same way.

Circle the verb which best fits the context of the following sentences.

8. Charlie _____, "Get out of my yard!" as the boys rode their bicycles over his petunias.

   remarked   replied   shouted   muttered   mumbled

9. When she saw Juan _____ across the dance floor in his new suit, Elena thought he was the most conceited boy she had ever seen.

   walk   hobble   march   strut   stride

10. The tired old woman _____ across the street.

    paced   strode   walked   strutted   hobbled

11. He _____ tears of joy when he heard the news.

    sobbed   wept   bawled   clamored   lamented

12. The bus was about to leave, but Robert _____ after it and got on just in time.

    ran   jogged   dashed   trotted   paced

18

13. Our car almost went off the road as the fire engine, its siren wailing, _____ past us down the steep hill.

breezed   crept   drove   roared   inched

14. Our windshield wipers were no match for the blinding snow as we _____ up the icy hill.

roared   drove   skimmed   inched   zipped

CONNOTATIONS AND DENOTATIONS

When choosing a specific word , we must pay attention to the *connotation* of a word. A word's CONNOTATION is made up of the ideas or feelings associated with the word. A word's DENOTATIONS are the actual meanings of the word, as found in the dictionary.

All words have at least one denotation, but not all words have strong connotations. A word may have different connotations for different people, depending on how they feel about the thing that word represents.

Words with strong connotations can be classified as positive (good) or negative (bad). For example, "skinny" and "scrawny" are insults since they have negative connotations, but "lean" and "slender" are compliments since they have positive connotations.

In the blank, write the letter of the word which correctly completes the sentence.

15. The _____ of a word can be looked up in the dictionary.

(A) connotation   (B) denotation

16. A word's _____ meaning includes the emotions people feel when they read that word.

(A) connotative   (B) denotative

17. The word "ring" _____ "a band worn around the finger."

(A) denotes   (B) connotes

18. *A dishonest person who is more interested in obtaining power and wealth than in working for improvements in society —* this is one _____ of "politican."

(A) denotation   (B) connotation

19. _____ of the word "hit" include (1) to beat or strike, and (2) something that is very popular, such as a record, a show, or a movie.

   (A) connotations   (B) denotations

20. A pig is an animal from which we obtain many food products. When the word "pig" is used to refer to someone, however, it _____ a person who is disgusting and ill-mannered.

   (A) connotes   (B) denotes

In the blank, write the letter of the word or expression which is more likely to have strong connotations.

21. (A) communist
    (B) diplomat   _____

22. (A) music
    (B) rock'n roll   _____

23. (A) person
    (B) teenager   _____

24. (A) jock
    (B) athlete   _____

25. (A) automobile
    (B) motorcycle   _____

26. (A) government
    (B) politics   _____

In the following pairs, circle the word which has a negative connotation.

27. thrifty   stingy

28. conceited   self-confident

29. stubborn   determined

30. aggressive   pushy

31. careful   fussy

32. skinny   slender

33. energetic   high-strung

34. carefree   reckless

35. inexpensive   cheap

36. tropical   sweltering

37. to joke   to make fun of

Under each sentence, check the word which has the proper connotation to fit the context. Then in the blank, write POSITIVE or NEGATIVE to describe the connotation of the word.

38. The _____ salesman annoyed several customers and sold very few cars last month.

        _____ (A) aggressive
        _____ (B) high-powered
        _____ (C) pushy   _____
        _____ (D) dedicated
        _____ (E) enthusiastic

39. The _____ of Jennifer's perfume made David think of lilacs in June.

        _____ (A) smell
        _____ (B) stench
        _____ (C) odor   _____
        _____ (D) fragrance
        _____ (E) stink

40. During the past year, Hugh has grown into a(n) _____, impressive-looking young man.

        _____ (A) lumbering
        _____ (B) strapping
        _____ (C) hulking   _____
        _____ (D) portly
        _____ (E) overgrown

41. My sister bought an expensive _____ clock to put over the fireplace in her new apartment.

        _____ (A) used
        _____ (B) dilapidated
        _____ (C) second-hand   _____
        _____ (D) antique
        _____ (E) old

4. Literal and Figurative Language

The literal meaning of a word is the real or actual meaning of a word. The literal meaning is similar to denotation. The opposite of literal is figurative. When a word is used figuratively, it is used in some way other than the ordinary meaning, to make a word picture or comparison.

The literal meaning of "pig" is "a fat, short-legged animal with a curly tail." If Barbara says, "My brother is such a pig!" she is using the word in a figurative way. Her brother is not literally a pig. Barbara is really saying that he's like a pig in some way.

A figurative use of language always involves a comparison between two things. Barbara's BROTHER is compared to a PIG; he is like a pig in some ways. The ROAD is compared to a RIBBON; it is long and narrow like a ribbon.

Try to use figurative language to make your own writing more interesting. Think of your own figures of speech rather than using expressions which people have heard over and over again. These overused expressions are called clichés. Clichés are trite or "corny" words or phrases. Avoid them in your writing.

Fill in the blanks with the word or letter that best completes each sentence.

1. The opposite of "figurative" is _____ .

2. "Literal" means about the same as _____ .

    (A) real or actual   (B) specific   (C) denotative   (D) A and C   (E) A, B, and C

3. An overused word or phrase is called a(n) _____ .

    (A) formality   (B) cliché   (C) alliteration   (D) denotation   (E) comparison

4. Figurative language works by using _____ .

    (A) connotation
    (B) comparisons
    (C) specific language
    (D) clichés

5. Your writing will improve if you DO NOT USE: _____ .

    (A) specific language
    (B) figurative language
    (C) clichés
    (D) formal English

One sentence in each of the following pairs uses the capitalized word literally. The other uses it figuratively.   Check the sentence that uses the word figuratively.

6. _____ Uncle Robert has GOLD fillings in his teeth.
   _____ Aunt Edna has a heart of GOLD.

7. _____ It was so COLD that the pipes froze.
   _____ She gave me a COLD stare and walked away.

8. _____ Sarah was GREEN with envy.
   _____ The leaves on the trees are GREEN in July.

9. _____ The CROWN she wore was made of emeralds, rubies, sapphires, diamonds, and gold.
   _____ The Scottish Highlanders rebelled against the CROWN in 1745.

10. _____ His arguments were FOOD for thought.
    _____ There was enough FOOD in the cabin to last for two weeks.

11. _____ Aunt Bee won her third award for the finest ROSES in the state.
    _____ The ROSES in her cheeks began to fade as she grew older in the harsh climate.

12. _____ He was a TOWER of strength to his family.
    _____ We visited the Leaning TOWER of Pisa while we were in Italy.

13. _____ The inspector left no STONE unturned in his investigation of the robbery.
    _____ Before planting the vegetables, we had to remove every STONE from the soil.

14. _____ You should talk to him about your garden, since he has such a GREEN thumb.
    _____ The driver was following the GREEN Honda in the left lane.

15. _____ He burnt his HANDS while washing the dishes.
    _____ All HANDS on deck!

16. _____ The white CHICKEN pecked for grain in the dust beside the road.
    _____ Sarah said that Sam was a CHICKEN because he wouldn't climb up to the tree house.

17. _____ Jason swept through the tidy room like a TORNADO.
    _____ A TORNADO swept through Xenia, Ohio, in 1973, destroying much of the town.

In the blank, write F if the sentence uses figurative language. Write L if the sentence is meant literally.

18. Terry goes to bed at 9:00 every evening.   _____

19. The narrow road is a ribbon stretched out between the fields.   _____

20. Rob is my father's right-hand man at the office.   _____

21. The book was not very interesting, so I returned it to the library.   _____

22. It's raining cats and dogs, so remember to take your umbrella.   _____

23. This box weighs a ton.   _____

24. I slept very soundly through the thunderstorm.   _____

25. My sister loves to cook; she has recipes coming out of her ears.   _____

26. It has been raining steadily for three days.   _____

27. He slept like a log after running in the marathon.   _____

Which things are compared in these examples of figurative language? In the blank, write the letter of the correct choice.

28. A soft pile of snow sat like a marshmallow on each fencepost.   _____

(A) A pile of snow is compared to a fencepost.
(B) A pile of snow is compared to a marshmallow.
(C) A marshmallow is compared to a fencepost.

29. How can a pile of snow be like a marshmallow?   _____

(A) Both are cold and wet.
(B) Both are soft white mounds.
(C) Both are sweet.

30. The huge truck jackknifed on the highway.   _____

    (A) The knife is compared to the highway.
    (B) The truck is compared to the highway.
    (C) The position of the truck is compared to a jackknife.

31. How can the position of a truck be like a jackknife?   _____

    (A) The truck is sharp.
    (B) The truck is bent like a half-open jackknife (like the letter V).
    (C) The truck is stuck in the road like a marshmallow.

32. The teachers felt as though they were drowning in papers.   _____

    (A) The teachers' work is compared to the students' work.
    (B) The papers are compared to the sea.
    (C) The papers are compared to the amount of work the students have.

33. How can papers make a teacher feel like he or she is drowning? _____

    (A) The papers may get wet and cause a mess.
    (B) The papers might be essays on water life.
    (C) There may be so many of them to mark that a teacher might feel overwhelmed.

Check the sentences which use figurative language.

34. _____ Their behavior at the party put a few noses out of joint.

35. _____ William Shakespeare wrote many famous plays.

36. _____ Emily's father hit the ceiling when he saw her report card.

37. _____ Raccoons like to hunt at night.

38. _____ After finishing work, everyone gathered at the new restaurant.

39. _____ I couldn't make heads or tails out of what he was saying.

40. _____ His little sister spilled the beans; now he is being punished.

41. _____ They stared at the figure on the T.V. screen.

42. _____ My uncle lives in the lap of luxury.

43. _____ The Yankees won both games last night.

44. _____ Janet has the Student Council election in the bag.

45. _____ I was unable to go because I had not yet finished my chores.

46. _____ The weather was balmy and beautiful all week long.

47. _____ He is generally very calm; it takes quite a bit to ruffle his feathers.

48. _____ A player from the other team gave him a real shiner during the football game.

In the space provided, finish each figure of speech in the best and most original way you can.

49. silent as (a) _____

50. The meal looked so unappealing that _____

51. slow as (a) _____

52. She had hair like _____

53. He eats like _____

54. as lovely as (a) _____

55. The day was as dismal as (a) _____

56. friendly as (a) _____

57. as dry as _____

58. The dough was so sticky that _____

59. as shiny as (a) _____

60. as pure as (a) _____

61. as greasy as (a) _____

62. as sparkling as (a) _____

5. Onomatopoeia and Alliteration

Another way to make your writing more interesting is to choose specific words that sound like the things you are trying to describe (onomatopoeia). Here are some examples of words that are onomatopoetic: boom, crash, splash, hiss, thud, tick.

Sometimes writers choose a word because it rhymes with another word or because it starts with the same letter or sound (alliteration). "Silly sister" is an example of alliteration. Some alliteration is effective; but do not use too much or your writing will sound like a tongue twister!

Check the answer that best completes each sentence.

1. The words "buzz," "thud," "ooze," and "splash" provide examples of

    _____ (A) onomatopoeia.
    _____ (B) alliteration.
    _____ (C) figures of speech.

2. "Tiny Tim" and "rascally rabbit" are examples of

    _____ (A) figurative language.
    _____ (B) alliteration.
    _____ (C) onomatopoeia.

3. Onomatopoeia and alliteration both have to do with

    _____ (A) the sounds of words.
    _____ (B) figurative language.
    _____ (C) literal language.

4. "Clammy cloud" is an example of

    _____ (A) a cliché.
    _____ (B) slang.
    _____ (C) alliteration.

5. *The steam HISSED from the pipes, and the water GURGLED down the drain.*
   The capitalized words were probably chosen for this sentence because they are

    _____ (A) onomatopoetic.
    _____ (B) slang.
    _____ (C) alliterative.

Circle the word which sounds best in each of the following sentences.

6. The snake _____ through the grass.

   rumbled   slithered   crept   coasted   fled

7. The low _____ of thunder far away warned us of the coming storm.

   rumble   crash   hiss   boom   roar

8. The spilled milk puddled on the table and quickly began to _____ onto the floor.

   dribble   drop   pour   slide   slosh

9. The river _____ over rocks and falls.

   coarses   bumps   flows   rambles   skips

10. I heard a(n) _____ from the archer's bow as he let go of the arrow.

    crack   twang   groan   click   echo

11. The butcher pounded the meat until he _____ it.

    softened   pulverized   kneaded   tenderized   flattened

12. She swam and _____ in the pool all afternoon after sunning herself all morning.

    floated   glided   lay   soaked   bathed

13. Janet heard the soda _____ as she poured it into the glass.

    fizz   rise   burst   glide   steam

14. He was kept awake all night by an owl _____ in the woods.

    crying   squawking   groaning   hooting   hissing

15. What a temper tantrum! He _____ and bawled until he got what he wanted.

    whined   bellowed   cried   pouted   grumbled

In the sentence pairs below, check the sentence which answers each question.

16. Which sentence uses rhyme?

    _____ (A) She looked about as elegant as an elephant.
    _____ (B) She looked about as elegant as a rhinoceros.

17. Which sentence uses onomatopoeia?

    _____ (A) As we approached the haunted house, we watched the door creak open.
    _____ (B) As we approached the haunted house, we watched the door slide open.

18. Which sentence uses alliteration?

    _____ (A) The quiet snow covered the town.
    _____ (B) The silent snow covered the city.

19. Which sentence uses alliteration (and onomatopoeia)?

    _____ (A) There I was, surrounded by noisy babies and howling kids.
    _____ (B) There I was, surrounded by babbling babies and crying kids.

20. Which sentence uses onomatopoeia?

    _____ (A) The ticking of the cuckoo clock was the only sound in the dark house.
    _____ (B) The only sound I could hear was the clock.

21. Which sentence uses alliteration?

    _____ (A) The snake slipped out of the cage and slithered away.
    _____ (B) The snake oozed out of the cage and crawled away.

22. Which sentence uses alliteration?

    _____ (A) She told us tales of terror through the night.
    _____ (B) She told us scary tales through the night.

23. Which sentence uses onomatopoeia?

    _____ (A) The delicate glass wind chimes were tinkling in the breeze.
    _____ (B) The delicate glass wind chimes were swinging in the breeze.

24. Which sentence uses onomatopoeia?

_____ (A) What kind of bird puts holes in wood?

_____ (B) What kind of bird pecks holes in wood?

25. Which sentence uses alliteration?

_____ (A) It often seems as though the branches of willow trees are dripping tears.

_____ (B) It often seems as though the branches of willow trees are weeping.

Before each sentence, put an O if the sentence contains onomatopoeia, an A if the sentence contains alliteration, or an N if the sentence contains neither.

26. _____ Aubrey has hair as black as ink.

27 _____ He is nothing but a sniveling, selfish coward.

28. _____ Josh received a hard slap on the back of his hand for stealing the fruit.

29. _____ The wind howled through the trees under a full moon.

30. _____ The crowd roared as the racers took off.

31. _____ Fiona sent his letter back to him without reading it.

32. _____ The drops fell with a plink from the kitchen faucet.

33. _____ We went to the green grocer's for some garden vegetables.

34. _____ Hugh did his homework, watched some T.V., and then went to bed.

35. _____ Duncan has a sullen face and a suspicious look about him.

36. _____ He felt an apple bonk him on the head while he slept under the tree.

37. _____ Tammy rode her bike home in the rain.

38. _____ A piece of pecan pie is perfect after a superb Thanksgiving dinner!

39. _____ It rained for three days and three nights.

40. _____ He's a fine figure of a man!

41. _____ The fans in the bleachers were whooping and howling at the players.

42. _____ She fell off her bed with a thud onto her stomach.

43. _____ She had seen the movie before on cable television but never in a theater.

44. _____ The generous gentleman was also gifted and gracious.

6. The Use of Formal Language

Written language is usually more formal than spoken language. Formal language follows certain rules, and is more "dressed up" than informal language. Use formal language in reports, essays, and business letters. You may use informal language in stories and friendly letters.

Here are some examples of formal and informal language:

INFORMAL	FORMAL
kids	children
guys	men
busted	arrested, broken
nosy	prying, inquisitive

Slang is very informal language. It consists of new words or old words used in new ways. Most slang expressions are popular for only a short time before they are replaced by new expressions. Different groups of people use different slang expressions. Avoid using slang in your writing unless you are trying to write the way people talk.

Fill in the blanks with the word or letter that best completes the sentence.

1. Formal is the opposite of _____ .

2. Which statement is true? _____

    (A) All writing uses formal language.
    (B) Informal language may be used in business letters.
    (C) Term papers and book reports should be written in formal English.
    (D) Informal language follows stricter rules than formal language.

3. _____ is very informal language, usually used in conversation.

4. Which is NOT true of most slang expressions? _____

    (A) They quickly come in and go out of style.
    (B) They can mean different things to different people.
    (C) They should be used in book reviews that you write for English class.
    (D) Many are types of figurative language.

5. The language in a report or in a business letter should be _____ .

In each of the pairs, put a check in front of the sentence which is the more formal.

6. _____ (A) The cops told the kids to move their bikes.
   _____ (B) The police told the children to move their bicycles.

7. _____ (A) Those guys like to hang out on this corner.
   _____ (B) Those men like to gather on this corner.

8. _____ (A) This book has a large amount of interesting material in it.
   _____ (B) This book has a lot of great stuff in it.

9. _____ (A) As they were led into the station, the crooks tried to make a break for it.
   _____ (B) As they were led into the station, the criminals tried to escape.

10. _____ (A) The author has some pretty weird ideas.
    _____ (B) The author has some rather peculiar ideas.

11. _____ (A) Charles told a senseless story, so I told him I did not understand.
    _____ (B) Charles told a dumb story, so I told him I didn't get it.

12. _____ (A) The party was a real drag, so we left early.
    _____ (B) The party was very boring, so we left early.

13. _____ (A) His behavior grosses me out.
    _____ (B) His behavior is disgusting.

14. _____ (A) I didn't like the story because the ending was so corny.
    _____ (B) I disliked the story because the ending was so trite.

15. _____ (A) She goofed off all year, so now she'll probably flunk.
    _____ (B) She fooled around all year, so now she will probably fail.

16. _____ (A) My little sister drives me crazy because she can be so irritating.
    _____ (B) My little sister drives me bananas because she can be a pain in the neck.

17. _____ (A) My goose is cooked if I don't find my science paper before I leave for school.
    _____ (B) I'll be in trouble if I don't find my science paper before I leave for school.

Circle the word or phrase which could be used to replace the capitalized slang word or expression.

18. This job could be A PIECE OF CAKE.

    (A) very easy   (B) fairly difficult   (C) good-tasting   (D) hard to cut

19. That movie really BLEW MY MIND.

    (A) amazed me   (B) annoyed me   (C) bored me   (D) put me to sleep

20. Jenny is too CHICKEN to climb that tree.

    (A) sensible   (B) cowardly   (C) clumsy   (D) young

21. The concert was TOTALLY AWESOME.

    (A) very exciting   (C) not loud enough   (D) too expensive   (D) empty

22. Every time she goes somewhere, she gets REALLY DECKED OUT.

    (A) very tired   (B) very dressed up   (C) very nervous   (D) too upset

23. He was making me so nervous, I finally told him to CHILL OUT.

    (A) take a swim   (B) eat something cold   (C) relax   (D) lose his temper

24. I can't work with him; he just can't GET WITH IT!

    (A) come late   (B) play a game properly   (C) pay attention   (D) goof around

25. People think she's STUCK UP, but she's actually just very shy.

    (A) snobby   (B) stupid   (C) friendly   (D) vulgar

26. She was so BUMMED OUT after she spoke to him on the phone.

    (A) sleepy   (B) amused   (C) disappointed   (D) excited

27. He was CHEWED OUT by the basketball coach yesterday.

    (A) cut from the team   (B) forgotten   (C) scolded   (D) praised

Check the sentences which use FORMAL English.

28. _____ Give me a break; don't make me read this junk!

29. _____ Mrs. Jones is a good teacher who always tries to be fair.

30. _____ This book is pretty good, but the ending is corny.

31. _____ Then she met this really great guy and they lived happily ever after.

32. _____ The movie is about this jerk who gets busted for dealing drugs.

33. _____ I enjoyed the book, but I thought the movie was uninteresting.

34. _____ The game was such a drag; we haven't lost by that much in a long time.

35. _____ They came back from the new skating rink and told us we should check it out.

36. _____ We printed every page as neatly and as clearly as we could.

37. _____ The whole thing just really burns me up.

38. _____ The principal got mad because we were horsing around in the cafeteria.

39. _____ His broken nose really stuck out like a sore thumb.

40. _____ The studio was greatly disappointed by the film's failure.

41. _____ The best reporter on the school paper had written the story.

42. _____ He got bounced from the team because he always missed practice.

43. _____ Left-handed children often face difficulties in adjusting to a right-handed world.

44. _____ She freaked out when she learned that Janet had bought the same dress she had.

45. _____ It was raining on Saturday, so I just hung around the house.

46. _____ *Origami* is a Japanese word that means "paper folding."

47. _____ Hoping for some news, Stewart ran home to look at the mail.

48. _____ I messed my leg up in soccer practice yesterday.

49. _____ The game was so unreal; they came from behind in the ninth inning.

50. _____ Some kid got expelled last week for smashing the windows in the library.

51. _____ The largest ferris wheel ever built was made by Gale Ferris in 1893.

52. _____ Few people came to the meeting yesterday.

SENTENCE CONSTRUCTION

7. Sentence Fragments and Run-on Sentences

Single words have little meaning out of context. A sentence provides context for a written word. A sentence is a group of words that expresses a complete thought. Each sentence must have a subject (the noun you are telling about) and a verb (what the subject is doing). A sentence should begin with a capital letter and end with a period, a question mark, or an exclamation point.

A sentence can be short, with only a subject and a verb. "Water freezes" is a sentence. "Water" is the subject that tells what the sentence is about. "Freezes" is the verb that tells what the subject is doing. In most sentences, the subject comes before the verb. When you are writing, do not write only a piece of a sentence, a sentence fragment. A fragment may be missing a subject, a verb, or both. Below are some examples of sentence fragments:

Drove all night through the rain. (subject missing; who drove?)
My third grade teacher, Miss Pierson. (verb missing; what did she do?)
In the corner, next to my chair. (no subject or verb; what is in the corner? what about it?)

A group of words can be a sentence fragment even if it has both a subject and a verb. In order to be a good sentence, a group of words must make sense by itself. "Unless Charlie arrived on time" is not a sentence even though it has a subject (Charlie) and a verb (arrived). "Charlie arrived on time" is a sentence.

A good sentence can be very long and still have one subject and one verb. "Jason laughed" is a sentence. "When Arthur told him the joke about the elephant and the football, Jason laughed so hard he almost passed out" is also a good sentence. In both sentences, "Jason" is the subject and "laughed" is the verb.

Write the word in the blank which correctly completes the following sentences.

1. A sentence provides the setting or _____ for a written word.

2. A sentence must express a complete _____ .

3. The noun you are telling about is called the _____ of the sentence.

4. Every sentence must contain a subject and a _____ .

5. Every sentence should begin with a _____ letter.

6. A sentence must end with a _____ , question mark, or exclamation point.

7. "During the early morning hours" is not a sentence. It is a sentence _____ .

Circle the subject (one word) and underline the verb (one word) in each sentence below.

8. Worn out from staying up so late, my mother slept right through the alarm.

9. The boy in the red shirt is the pitcher on our team.

10. The wild horses stampeded across the meadow.

11. Lisa bought the red convertible from her neighbor Mr. Cummings.

12. Lean and hungry, the wolves howled at the Arctic moon.

13. Exhausted after the race, I collapsed on the grass.

14. Suddenly, a motorcycle approached from the opposite direction.

15. The three girls in the corner giggled at the joke.

16. The pizza tastes better without anchovies.

17. Hugh rode his bicycle up to Newport over the weekend.

In the space provided, write SV if the subject comes before the verb. If the verb comes first, re-write the words in subject-verb order.

EXAMPLE: ran dogs
ANSWER: dogs ran

18. birds fly

19. fell it

20. Jason laughed

21. called she

22. gasped people

23. the bell rang

24. fell leaves

What is missing in each of the following fragments? In the space provided, write S for subject, V for verb, SV for both.

25. Next to Uncle Fred's house.   _____

26. All my first cousins.   _____

27. Hit her head on the shelf.   _____

28. Some day in the future.   _____

29. Joanne and my sister's friends.   _____

30. Ran out the door with a bucket of water.   _____

31. If it were up to me.   _____

32. Scored several goals at the game yesterday.   _____

33. Depending on the weather.   _____

After each group of words, write F if they form a fragment, S if they form a sentence.

34. Unless Charlie arrives on time, we will cancel the performance.   _____

35. If we win next Thursday's game.   _____

36. Behind the house was a small shed.   _____

37. Knowing very little about the subject.   _____

38. The clouds disappeared by noon.   _____

39. The phone rang only three times.   _____

40. After we went to the museum.   _____

41. She finished her work with my help.   _____

42. Even though they tried their best.   _____

43. Running round and round the track.   _____

44. The picture book on the shelf.   _____

45. I polished my shoes last night.   _____

46. Down the hill as fast as possible.   _____

RUN-ON SENTENCES

When you write longer sentences, be careful not to run several sentences together. The run-on error is the opposite of the fragment error. A fragment stops before it is a complete sentence. A run-on includes at least two complete sentences. Run-ons do not have to be long. Often, writers create run-ons by connecting two short sentences with a comma, as in the following example:

Don't turn on the television, you will wake up my father.

Two words that often cause run-ons are "it" and "then." The examples below are run-ons:

My brother bought a new car, it is a Cadillac.
Finish the dishes, then sweep the floor.

There are several ways to fix a run-on. The easiest way is to split it into two sentences.

RUN-ON: *I looked through every pocket, my ticket was gone.*
CORRECT: *I looked through every pocket. My ticket was gone.*

Another way to fix a run-on is to join the two sentences with a comma and a conjunction ("and," "but," or "or.") The result is called a compound sentence, a sentence made up of several sentences joined together.

A third way to fix a run-on is to join the two sentences with a semicolon (;). Use a semicolon only if the two sentences are short and are closely connected in meaning.

EXAMPLE: *Writing can be difficult; talking is easier.*

Fill in the blank with the word that correctly completes the sentence.

47. A _____ sentence includes at least two complete sentences.

48. What form of punctuation is most often used in a run-on sentence?

_____ (A) semicolon
_____ (B) period
_____ (C) comma

49. Writers can split run-on sentences by using:

_____ (A) commas or semi-colons.
_____ (B) periods or semi-colons.
_____ (C) commas or periods.

50. Writers can fix run-on sentences by adding _____ after a comma.

51. If a conjunction is added to a run-on sentence, the result is a _____ sentence.

In the blank provided, write R if the word group below is a run-on, S if it is a sentence.

52. I parked the car when I got back, it was gone. _____

53. Everyone in my family has a birthday in June. _____

54. Sarah looked at her notes then she began to speak. _____

55. If you turn on the television, you will wake up my father. _____

56. Three of my friends are coming over, they will be here soon. _____

57. This car is economical, it uses very little gas. _____

58. Tammy is allowed to go, I have to finish my chores. _____

59. During the past week, several classmates have become sick. _____

60. The book I bought was interesting, it has some lovely pictures. _____

61. If you see your brother, tell him that the game starts at noon. _____

62. I have your book at home, it wasn't stolen. _____

Check the run-on sentence in each set of examples.

63. _____ (A) I like our new house because it is bright and cheerful.
    _____ (B) I like our new house, it is bright and cheerful.
    _____ (C) Because it is so bright and cheerful, I really like our new house.

64. _____ (A) Mark first wrote his papers in pencil, then he copied them in ink.
    _____ (B) After first writing his papers in pencil, Mark copied them in ink.
    _____ (C) Mark copied his papers over in ink after first writing them in pencil.

65. _____ (A) I have heard this joke several times, it still seems funny.
    _____ (B) I have heard this joke several times, but it still seems funny.
    _____ (C) Even though I have heard this joke several times, it still seems funny.

66. _____ (A) I called you, but you hadn't arrived home yet.
    _____ (B) When I called you, you hadn't arrived home yet.
    _____ (C) I called you, you hadn't arrived home yet.

67. _____ (A) She wore the dress, although she didn't like it.
    _____ (B) She didn't like the dress, she wore it anyway.
    _____ (C) She didn't like the dress, but she wore it anyway.

Insert a period in each of the run-on sentences below to make two correct sentences.
You may want to correct the capitalization in each sentence as well.

68. James didn't come his parents would not let him.

69. I touched the mysterious box it moved away from my hand.

70. The dog barked loudly then it wagged its tail.

71. The box was open the money was gone.

72. Some people go to college others don't.

73. There is no air or water on the moon nothing can live there.

74. We went to the library to check out some books then we went grocery shopping.

75. It looks as though it might rain the sky is growing darker by the minute.

76. I won't be able to go to the movies I don't have enough money for the tickets.

77. She asked me where he was I told her I did not know.

For each of the sentences below, add the conjunction (and, or, or but) that makes the most sense. You will need to add punctuation to some sentences.

78. The car was old, _____ it needed to be repaired.

79. We can send this letter _____ we can call on the telephone.

80. George tried to put the baby to bed _____ she wouldn't go to sleep.

81. I'll take the bus _____ ride my bike. It depends on the weather.

82. He played basketball, _____ then we went for a hike in the woods.

Correct the run-ons below by inserting a semicolon.

83. The word "accept" means one thing the word "except" means something else.

84. This book is really exciting I read it all in one day.

85. Helen doesn't want this magazine give it to Marcia.

86. I don't know if I can go to the dance I'll have to see if my brother can drive me.

87. I enjoy photography very much it allows me to look at things from a different viewpoint.

Indicate whether each of the following word groups is a:

> *(F) fragment*
> *(R) run-on*
> *(S) sentence*

88. Stopping the car just in time. _____

89. I can't get to the store by noon, maybe I can get a ride later on. _____

90. If Charles and Jeff don't work harder, the job won't get done. _____

91. The book was fascinating, but the movie was boring. _____

92. Mr. Jenkins, the elderly English teacher who lives next door. _____

93. Robert typed the report then he handed it in. _____

94. If Helen doesn't want this magazine, then give it to Marcia. _____

95. Tom's speech was excellent, everyone applauded. _____

96. Driving down the steep mountain road with his brakes screeching. _____

97. Their house was destroyed by the hurricane, but ours was not even damaged. _____

98. Even though Mrs. Smith knew her help was not wanted. _____

99. Probably a racoon or a squirrel. _____

100. I couldn't see a thing out the window it was raining so hard. _____

101. Before the movie started. _____

102. He took the high road, and I took the low road. _____

103. That he had stolen the fruit. _____

104. She put her clothes away before she went to bed. _____

105. I do not like the way she sings, it is too loud and shrill. _____

106. Why did you paint it purple, you know that is my least favorite color? _____

107. Venetia told me to make two copies by noon, I know I won't finish by then. _____

8. Compound Sentences and Verbs

A sentence may have more than one subject or verb even if it is not made up of two or more connected sentences (a compound sentence). A sentence with two or more subjects or verbs is said to have a compound subject or a compound verb.

EXAMPLES: *James and I fished all night.* (compound subject)
James fished all night and slept all day. (compound verb)
James, Charlie, and I fished all night and slept all day.
(compound subject and compound verb)

Two sentences can often be combined to form one more interesting sentence by forming compound subjects and verbs.

EXAMPLES: *Jill is a good tennis player.*
Ben is a good tennis player, too.
COMBINED: *Jill and Ben are good tennis players.*

Other parts of a sentence can also be compounds. When more than two words or phrases are joined to make a series, put a comma after each word or phrase except the last one. Put the word "and," "but," or "or" before the last word or phrase.

EXAMPLE: For breakfast, I like waffles, bacon, orange juice, and milk.

Write the word in the blank which correctly completes the following sentences.

1. A sentence may have more than one subject and more than one _____ .

2. If a sentence has more than one subject, it is said to have a _____ subject.

3. When two sentences are joined correctly, with a comma and a conjunction or with a semicolon (;), the combined sentence is called a _____ sentence.

4. In the first example above, "James" and "I" form the compound _____ .

5. In the second example above, "fished" and "slept" form the compound _____ .

6. Which punctuation is used to separate items in a series within a compound sentence?

_____ (A) semi-colons
_____ (B) periods
_____ (C) commas

Underline the compound subject (two words) in each of the following sentences.

7. Robert's little brother and sister are twins.

8. The old car and the rusty van were sold for scrap metal.

9. In the afternoon, Jennifer and I often go to the park.

10. Vivian and I are going to go to the party with Lynn on Saturday night.

11. The wind and the rain battered the houses along the shore.

12. Sam's math book and calculator sat on his desk.

13. A tall gymnast and a short basketball player met while walking into the gym.

14. In our office Steve P. and Steve G. are constantly receiving each other's mail.

Underline the compound verb (two words) in each of the following sentences.

15. Last summer we drove to Yellowstone Park and camped there for a week.

16. I went to the library and found three books on our list.

17. Sarah likes Jason but hates George.

18. I made the bread but ate only the crackers.

19. Emily did the dishes and studied her French after dinner.

20. As punishment, the boys had to clean the school cafeteria and work in the library .

21. I called her and wrote her a letter over the weekend.

22. He dusted and vacuumed before the guests arrived.

Fill in the missing word or words in the combined sentences below.

23. Mark likes to play soccer. Mark hates to play football.

    Mark likes to play _____ but _____ to play football.

24. Barbara went to the movies last night. Marty went with her.

    Barbara _____ _____ went to the movies last night.

25. Tony is going shopping. Ken is going shopping. Robin is going, too.

    Tony, Ken, and _____ _____ _____ _____ .

26. I bought tickets to the play yesterday. Joanne came with me to buy her own tickets.

    _____ _____ I bought tickets to the play yesterday.

27. Jonathan plays soccer after dinner each evening. His son, Ricky, plays with him.

    Jonathan _____ _____ _____, _____,

    play soccer together after dinner each evening.

Fill in the missing words and commas in the combined sentences below.

28. I have read the book. I have not seen the movie.

    I have read the book but   the movie.

29. He brought the tools in from the rain. He brought the wheelbarrow in from the rain.

    He brought   in from
    the rain.

30. David is studying English and science. He is also studying Spanish and algebra.

    David is studying English, science

31. Sand was in my hair. Sand was in my shoes. Sand was in the cuffs of my blue jeans.

    Sand was in my hair, in   and in the cuffs of my blue jeans.

45

32. My pockets were full of change. My pockets were full of tissue paper.

My pockets were full of

In the space provided, label each sentence A, B, C, or D.

    (A) compound sentence (two or more complete sentences joined correctly)
    (B) sentence with a compound subject
    (C) sentence with a compound verb
    (D) none of the above

33. Beets and broccoli do not taste good on pizza.   _____

34. Diana gasped for breath and groped for the entrance to the cave.   _____

35. I thought she told me to come over after dinner.   _____

36. I put peppers, anchovies, and onions on my pizza.   _____

37. The pizza was good, but the service was terrible.   _____

38. My sister has lived and traveled all over Asia.   _____

39. When I moved to the Southwest, I missed the changing of the seasons.   _____

40. When we were in school, Rita and I played hockey and lacrosse together.   _____

41. Beth and Ricky went to their father's office to use the copier and computer.   _____

42. She loved her new haircut, but everyone else thought she looked ridiculous.   _____

43. I bought a new winter coat, some boots, and a warm pair of gloves.   _____

44. The snow and sleet made driving very dangerous.   _____

45. She does not like to write letters to her friends.   _____

46. He picked himself up, dusted off his shirt, and went back into the game.   _____

47. It was a very chilly day, but the sun was shining brightly.   _____

48. I received and spent my allowance on school supplies and some new clothes.   _____

49. His books and lunch box fell off the back of his bike as he stopped.   _____

50. We could go to a movie, or we could play chess.   _____

9. Modifiers

Combining short, simple sentences can help you to write without using unnecessary words. One way to combine sentences is to drop the words being repeated by putting all the modifiers (adjectives and adverbs) into one sentence.

EXAMPLE: The children climbed the hill. The children were tired. The hill was steep.
COMBINED: The tired children climbed the steep hill.

Several modifiers can be put in front of one noun: "disgustingly greasy pizza"; "four red cars." Do not overdo this with too many modifiers, as in "a very short, ugly, thin, blond, freckled girl."

Two or more modifiers in front of a noun are often separated by commas. You can tell whether or not to use a comma. If you can reverse the order of the modifiers, or connect them with "and," you should use a comma. Do not put a comma right before the noun.

EXAMPLE: a hungry, tired girl OR a tired, hungry girl OR a hungry and tired girl
BUT NOT two, blue cars OR two and blue cars

Prepositional phrases such as "under the table," "in the park," and "for the moment" are also modifiers. They can be put in different positions in a sentence.

EXAMPLE: The boy was hiding. He was hiding IN THE BUSHES.
COMBINED: 1) The boy was hiding IN THE BUSHES.
2) The boy IN THE BUSHES was hiding.
3) IN THE BUSHES, the boy was hiding.

There are other ways to add modifiers.

EXAMPLES: 1) The HOT, TIRED boys finally slept.
2) HOT AND TIRED, the boys finally slept.
3) The boys, HOT AND TIRED, finally slept.
4) The boys finally slept, HOT AND TIRED.

Fill in the blank with the word which correctly completes the sentence below.

1. One way to combine sentences is by putting all the _____ and adverbs into one sentence.

2. Adjectives and adverbs are also known as _____ .

3. If you are using more than one modifier, separate them with _____ .

4. Which of the phrases below does NOT need commas?

_____ (A) three sad clowns
_____ (B) rich young pilot
_____ (C) frightened hungry kitten

Write the adjective or adverb which is missing in the following sentences. Add punctuation where it is needed.

EXAMPLE: A dog bounded down the path. The dog was a Great Dane. It was huge. The path was narrow.
COMBINED: The _____ Great Dane bounded down the _____ path.
ANSWER: The ***huge*** Great Dane bounded down the ***narrow*** path.

5. We will never order the fried chicken again. The fried chicken is greasy.

   We will never order the _____ fried chicken again.

6. Al's brother gives up when he starts to lose a game. Al's brother is older than he is. He gives up immediately.

   Al's _____ brother gives up _____ when he starts to lose a game.

7. The ships came into harbor. The ships were tall. They were noble also.

   The _____ , _____ ships came into harbor.

8. We bought bait for our fishing trip. The bait was fresh. The trip was over the weekend.

   We bought _____ bait for our _____ fishing trip.

9. Writers went to the pep rally. The writers were eager. They worked for the school paper.

   _____ writers for the _____ paper went to the pep rally.

10. The lake was frozen. It was perfect for ice-skating. We liked to skate at nighttime.

    The _____ lake was perfect for _____ ice-skating.

11. A witch gazed at Dorothy. The witch was evil. The witch was old.

    The _____ _____ witch gazed at Dorothy.

12. The violinist played in the band. He was blind. He was young.

    The _____ _____ violinist played in the band.

13. People walked in and looked at him. Many did. They were all well-dressed.

    _____ _____ people walked in and looked at him.

Fill in the modifiers which should go in front of each noun in the following sentences. Add punctuation where it is needed.

14. Men sat in front of the courthouse. Three men sat there. The men were fat. They were extremely fat.

    _____ _____ _____ men sat in front of the courthouse.

15. The weather made us all want to go to sleep. The weather was hot. It was unbearably hot.

    The _____ _____ weather made us all want to go to sleep.

16. He told a story at dinner. The story was long. The story was boring. The story was unbelievably long.

    He told an _____ _____ _____ story at dinner.

17. We approached the spooky house. We approached the deserted house. We approached with caution.

    We _____ approached the _____ _____ house.

18. Her mother made her wear the dress. The dress was baggy. The dress was green.

    Her mother made her wear the _____ _____ dress.

19. Three boys fell into the pool. The boys were blond. They fell by accident.

    _____ _____ boys _____ fell into the pool.

49

20. He made a towel rack out of a ladder. The ladder was broken. The ladder was wooden. The ladder was old.

He made a towel rack out of an _____ _____

_____ ladder.

21. Her two friends were throwing a party for her. They were her best friends. The party was a surprise.

Her two _____ friends were throwing a _____ party for her.

Fill in the prepositional phrase for each of the following sentences. In some of the sentences you may have to change the preposition before the sentence makes sense.

22. All the bells rang. They rang for one minute.

_____ _____ _____, all the bells rang.

23. The sweater was a birthday present. It was a present from my mother.

The sweater was a birthday present _____ _____ _____ .

24. The old mansion will be torn down. It is near the park. It will be torn down in August.

In August, the old mansion _____ _____ _____ will be torn down.

25. Mr. Perlman performs on the violin. He has performed in many countries.

Mr. Perlman has performed on the violin _____ _____

_____ .

26. I borrowed the library book. I borrowed it from Amy.

I borrowed the library book _____ _____ .

27. I lent my albums to Sarah. She will play them at her party.

I lent my albums to Sarah _____ _____ _____ .

28. The children were hiding. They were behind the sofa. The sofa was in the living room.

The children were hiding _____ _____ _____

_____ _____ .

29. Two cowboys rode into town. They were wearing black hats.

Two cowboys _____ _____ _____ rode into town.

30. Dianne was at the door. She was listening to her sisters plan a practical joke.

_____ _____ _____ , Dianne was listening to her sisters plan a practical joke.

Fill in the blank with the word or words which correctly complete the combined sentences.

31. The dog limped home. The dog was exhausted.

_____ , the dog limped home.

32. Their banner fluttered in the breeze. It was blue. It was also gold.

_____ _____ _____ , their banner fluttered in the breeze.

33. The first graders sat up straight in their chairs. They were eager. They were excited.

_____ _____ _____ , the first graders sat up straight in their chairs.

34. She was weary. She was wet. She returned home from her bike ride in the rain.

_____ _____ _____ , she returned home from her bike ride in the rain.

35. Doug was concerned about the rain. Doug went home to make certain his basement was not flooding.

_____ _____ _____ _____ ,

Doug went home to make certain that his basement was not flooding.

51

36. *The House at Pooh Corner* was written by A. A. Milne. *The House at Pooh Corner* is a popular children's book.

   _____ _____ _____ _____ _____, *The House at Pooh Corner* is a popular children's book.

37. Lucy was leaning against the piano. Lucy was listening to him play a song he had written.

   _____ _____ _____, Lucy was listening to him play a song he had written.

38. Josh was running around the bases. He was thinking only of making a home run.

   _____ _____ _____ _____, Josh was thinking only of making a home run.

10. Relative Clauses

A clause is a group of words with a subject and a verb. Clauses beginning with the words "who," "which," "that," "whose," and "whom" are very useful when combining two sentences.

EXAMPLE: The newspaper had a picture of the accident.
             I bought the newspaper this morning.
COMBINED: The newspaper which I bought this morning had a picture of the accident.
OR   The newspaper that I bought this morning had a picture of the accident.

"Which" replaces nouns that refer to things and animals. "Who" replaces nouns that refer to people. "That" can replace nouns that refer to either people or things. "Whose" replaces nouns that show possession (car's, cat's) and refers to people, animals, or things. "Whom" replaces nouns that refer to people. "Whom" is the object of the verb and can often be omitted or replaced by "that."

EXAMPLE: The people whom I met were polite. OR The people I met were polite.
             The people that I met were polite.

Notice how the sentences below are combined:

EXAMPLE: Mr. Johnson teaches science. He is my favorite teacher.
COMBINED: 1) Mr. Johnson, who is my favorite teacher, teaches science.
             2) Mr. Johnson, who teaches science, is my favorite teacher.

The sentences above can be written a shorter way if we drop the subject and verb of the second sentence (He is). If we choose to drop the subject and the verb of the second sentence, then we no longer have a *clause* . (Remember that a clause must have a subject *and* a verb.) If we choose to do this, then we have an *appositive*.

COMBINED: 1) Mr. Johnson, my favorite teacher, teaches science.
             2) My favorite teacher, Mr. Johnson, teaches science.

Fill in the blank with the word or letter that best completes the sentence.

1. A _____ is a group of words with a subject and a verb.

2. _____ can be used when referring to people.

    _____ (A) "Who" or "which"
    _____ (B) "Which" or "that"
    _____ (C) "Who" or "that"

3. "Whose" can be used to refer to:

    _____ (A) only people.
    _____ (B) people or things.
    _____ (C) people, animals, or things.

4. An appositive is _____ a clause.

   _____ (A) shorter than
   _____ (B) longer than
   _____ (C) the same as

5. An appositive uses _____ .

   _____ (A) commas
   _____ (B) a subject or a verb
   _____ (C) "who," whose," or "whom"

Circle the words in the second sentence which have been repeated and could be replaced.

6. Aesop's fables all have morals. In Aesop's fables, the animals act like human beings.

7. The invading Martians roam the earth in machines. The machines look like water towers.

8. Gypsies were nomads from India. Gypsies migrated into Europe.

9. Cystic fibrosis is an hereditary disease. Cystic fibrosis is fatal.

10. He found the star. The star formed the top of the Big Dipper's handle.

11. Danny has a cat. Danny's cat has no tail.

12. The new neighbors moved in yesterday. The neighbors are coming for dinner tonight.

13. I have a cookbook. My cookbook lists twenty recipes from China.

14. He went to water the marigolds. The marigolds had just been planted.

15. Gary was wearing the new sweater. His aunt had knit the new sweater for him.

16. We found the flag. The flag belonged to the opposing team.

17. I finally finished the geography project. The geography project is due tomorrow.

18. Shawn can run faster than Willy. Willy's brother is the fastest runner in the class.

Fill in the blanks with "which" or "who," and with any other missing words.

19. The Martians roamed the earth in machines. The machines looked like water towers.

    The Martians roamed the earth in machines _____ _____ like water towers.

20. Gypsies were nomads from India. Gypsies migrated into Europe.

    Gypsies were nomads from _____ _____ _____ into Europe.

21. Cystic fibrosis is an hereditary disease. This disease is fatal.

    Cystic fibrosis is an hereditary disease _____ _____ _____ .

22. He found the star. The star formed the top of the Big Dipper's handle.

    He found the star _____ _____ the top of the Big Dipper's handle.

23. Danny has a cat. Danny's cat has no tail.

    Danny has a cat _____ _____ _____ _____.

24. The new neigbors moved in yesterday. The neighbors are coming for dinner tonight.

    The new neighbors _____ _____ _____ yesterday are coming for dinner tonight.

25. I have a cookbook. My cookbook lists twenty recipes from China.

    I have a cookbook _____ _____ _____ recipes from China.

26. He went to water the marigolds. The marigolds had just been planted.

   He went to water the marigolds_____ _____ _____ _____

   _____ .

27. Gary was wearing the new sweater. His aunt had knit the new sweater for him.

   Gary was wearing the new sweater _____ _____ _____ _____
   knit for him.

Fill in the blank with "who," "whom," or "whose."

28. The ambulance picked up the boy. The boy's leg was broken.

   The ambulance picked up the boy _____ leg was broken.

29. The man went around the corner. I was following the man.

   The man _____ I was following went around the corner.

30. The man went around the corner. I was following the man.

   I was following the man _____ went around the corner.

31. The woman was delighted at the news. The woman's roses had won first prize.

   The woman _____ roses had won first prize was delighted.

32. My mother makes chili. Her chili could burn a hole through your tongue. She loves hot
   food.

   My mother, _____ chili could burn a hole through your tongue, loves hot
   food.

33. I was inviting some freinds. The friends lived almost ten miles away.

   The friends _____ I was inviting lived almost ten miles away.

Each of the following sentences should have two commas. Add the missing comma, and circle the word that comes BEFORE the comma.

34. Albert, who is a fireman was injured on the job.

35. Today Mr. Santos who is my supervisor, told me I would be promoted.

36. The newspapers, which are stacked in the garage are ready to be recycled.

37. Her brother who is a talented carpenter, built the bookshelves in our living room.

38. Mr. Grimanis, who left teaching last week is getting married in two months.

39. The sky, which had grown black as pitch warned of the approaching tornado.

40. Charlene, who had gotten the hiccups could not finish the game.

Fill in the words which correctly complete the combined sentences below.

41. David Lee sits next to me. He is my best friend.

   David Lee, _____ , sits next to me.

42. Robert's camera was stolen from his locker. The camera was a Pentax.

   Robert's camera, _____ , was stolen from his locker.

43. Mrs. Elliott gave a lecture. She is the president of the Foreman Company.

   Mrs. Elliott, _____ , gave a lecture.

44. I have read *Kidnapped* five times. *Kidnapped* is my favorite book.

   I have read *Kidnapped*, _____ , five times.

45. Ross proudly showed one of his birthday presents to his friends. One of his birthday presents was his grandfather's wristwatch.

   Ross proudly showed one of his birthday presents, _____ ,

   to his friends.

46. The book has already been checked out of the library. The book is a biography of Aaron Burr.

The book, _____ , has already been checked out of the library.

47. Tammy is a talented gymnast. Tammy won four medals at last year's state championship.

Tammy, _____ , won four medals at last year's state championship.

48. After dinner, I want to go to the movie. The movie is a science fiction thriller.

After dinner, I want to go to the movie, _____

49. The show this year will be in Harrisburg. Harrisburg is the capital of Pennsylvania.

The show this year will be in Harrisburg, _____

11. Subordinating Conjunctions

Another way to combine sentences is to connect them with a subordinating conjunction. Ten of the most common ones are: *because, since, although, if, unless, when, while, before, after,* and *until.*

"Subordinate" means "less important." The clause that starts with a subordinating conjunction becomes less important than the main clause, the clause that does not start with a subordinating conjunction. A main (or independent) clause can be a sentence on its own. A subordinate (or dependent) clause cannot be a sentence by itself. A subordinate clause can come at the beginning or at the end of a sentence. Put a comma after a subordinate clause that comes at the beginning of a sentence. Do not put a comma between two clauses if the main clause comes first.

EXAMPLE: Because our car was insured, we did not lose any money.
We did not lose any money because our car was insured.

A sentence with a main clause and a subordinate clause is called a complex sentence. A sentence with two (or more) main clauses joined with "and," "but," "or," or a semicolon is a compound sentence. A simple sentence has only one clause. Try to use complex sentences rather than compound sentences when you write. Complex sentences let you express more specific relationships between ideas or actions. They let you say which of two ideas is more important by putting it in the main clause. The less important idea goes in the subordinate clause.

Check the letter of the answer that best completes the sentence.

1. The _____ is the more important clause of the sentence.

    _____ (A) subordinate clause
    _____ (B) main clause

2. The _____ can stand on its own as a grammatically correct sentence.

    _____ (A) subordinate clause
    _____ (B) main clause

3. A _____ starts with such words as "because," "while," "after," and "until."

    _____ (A) subordinate clause
    _____ (B) main clause

4. In a sentence with a subordinate clause, commas are needed when

    _____ (A) the main clause comes before the subordinate clause.
    _____ (B) the subordinate clause comes first.

5. A complex sentence is one which contains:

    _____ (A) two main clauses.
    _____ (B) two subordinate clauses.
    _____ (C) a subordinate and a main clause.

6. _____ sentences are ones which use subordinate conjunctions, such as "because" and "since."

    _____ (A) Compound
    _____ (B) Complex

7. The use of _____ clauses describes more clear and specific relationships between ideas.

    _____ (A) subordinate
    _____ (B) main

Fill in the blank with the subordinating conjunction which best completes the following sentences.

8. I dressed Bobby for bed. Then he wanted to go outside.

    _____ I dressed Bobby for bed, he wanted to go outside.

9. Pat slept with his parents during the storm. He was afraid of the thunder.

    Pat slept with his parents during the storm _____ he was afraid of the thunder.

10. Marcia went on a strict diet. She didn't lose any weight.

    _____ Marcia went on a strict diet, she didn't lose any weight.

11. They made sure that everything was turned off. Then they left for vacation.

    _____ they left for vacation, they made sure that everything was turned off.

12. We cannot leave for the beach. We have to wait for Dad to return from the dentist.

   We cannot leave for the beach _____ Dad returns from the dentist.

13. Dan barbecued the chicken. His friends were playing volleyball.

   _____ his friends were playing volleyball, Dan barbecued the chicken.

Indicate whether the capitalized clause in each of the following sentences is a:

   (A) subordinate (dependent) clause
   (B) main (independent) clause

14. When the car stopped abruptly, MY HEAD HIT THE WINDSHIELD. _____

15. Janet breaks out in a rash IF SHE EATS TOO MANY STRAWBERRIES. _____

16. BECAUSE OUR CAR WAS INSURED, we did not lose any money. _____

17. UNLESS IT RAINS THIS WEEK, we will lose our vegetable crops. _____

18. I DON'T LIKE PLAYING WITH DEREK because he is too competitive. _____

19. We grabbed a bite to eat BEFORE WE LEFT FOR THE MOVIE. _____

20. Until he buys a bike, HE WILL DELIVER HIS PAPERS ON FOOT. _____

In each of the following sentences, add a comma if you think one is needed. If a comma is not needed, write NO COMMA by the sentence.

21. After she did her laundry she went to the grocer's to pick up some vegetables.

22. Although Ann wanted to be a surgeon, she couldn't dissect a frog.

23. Once people learn to ride a bicycle, they never forget.

24. If David gets a better job he can afford to buy a new car.

25. Sharon was late to the party because she got lost twice.

26. Arthur my brother's dog, hides under the couch when visitors come.

27. Though Mark now directs plays he used to be a professional actor.

28. Until he admits that he cheated I won't play cards with him anymore.

29. Janet could not go on the hike because she had misplaced her boots.

30. He brought the lawn furniture in before it started to rain.

Indicate whether each of the following sentences is a:

    (A) simple sentence   (B) compound sentence   (C) complex sentence

31. After he finished the dishes, Jim swept the floor. _____

32. Jim finished the dishes, and then he swept the floor. _____

33. Jim finished the dishes and swept the floor. _____

34. He could not rake the lawn until his father had cut the grass. _____

35. His father cut the grass, and then he raked the lawn. _____

Finish converting the following compound sentences to complex sentences by drawing a circle around the subordinating conjunction that best completes each sentence.

36. Charles can be obnoxious, but I still like him.

    I still like Charles _____ he can be obnoxious.

        unless   because   even though   when

37. I get home from school, and I do my homework.

    _____ I get home from school, I do my homework.

        Before   While   Until   After

38. We kept on searching, and we found the missing ring.

    We kept on searching _____ we found the missing ring.

           while   because   until   after

39. The sky was blue and clear, but the weatherman was predicting rain.

    _____ the sky was blue and clear, the weatherman was predicting rain.

           Since   Although   Unless   Before

40. We cannot go roller skating now. We have to wait for Brian's swimming lesson to end.

    We cannot go roller skating _____ Brian's swimming lesson ends.

           unless   because   while   until

12. Participial Phrases

Sentences are also combined in the following ways:

EXAMPLE: I walked around the block. I looked for my cousin.
COMBINED: 1) Walking around the block, I looked for my cousin.
                2) I walked around the block, looking for my cousin.

To combine sentences in this way, change one of the verbs to a present participle, which always starts with the verb's present tense and ends with "-ing." For example, change *run* to *running* and *saw* to *seeing*.

After changing the verb to a present participle, drop the subject of the sentence. The resulting group of words is a participial phrase. A phrase can never be a sentence because it does not have a subject or a verb. A participle is not a verb; it's only part of a verb.

SENTENCE: The boys drove to Boston.
PARTICIPIAL PHRASE: driving to Boston

You need to put a comma after a participial phrase that is at the beginning of a sentence. When such a phrase is at the end of a sentence, use a comma before the phrase only if it is NOT next to the noun it is modifying.

ONE COMMA: Running through the woods, the boy soon became frightened.
TWO COMMAS: The boy, running through the woods, soon became frightened.
NO COMMA: The boy met a bear running through the woods.

Sentences can also contain <u>past</u> participial phrases. Past participles usually end in "-ed," "-en," or "-n."

VERB	PRESENT PARTICIPLE	PAST PARTICIPLE
open	opening	opened
fall	falling	fallen
break	breaking	broken

EXAMPLE: James was confused by the directions. He failed the test.
COMBINED: Confused by the directions, James failed the test.

In the space provided, write the present participle of the verb in each sentence below.

1. The boys drove to Boston.

2. The woman left the store.

3. They scrubbed the floor.

4. She read the book yesterday.

5. I painted the garage.

Change each short sentence below to a participial phrase by dropping the subject and changing the verb to a present participle.

6. Sharon heard the bell ring.

7. Janie went to the store. (HINT: What is the present tense of "went"?)

8. The pig was sitting in a puddle.

9. He held his head in his hands.

10. Peter got into the car.

11. Venetia made a pot of spaghetti.

12. She tried to repair the toaster.

13. Duncan was folding the laundry.

14. Steve printed the programs.

15. He pulled the pliers out of the toolbox.

In each of the following sentences, add a comma if you think one is needed. If a comma is not needed, write NO COMMA by the sentence.

16. Hearing footsteps Jason hid in the closet.

17. Hoping for a victory, the team captain gave an enthusiastic pep talk.

18. We saw the cat climbing the apple tree.

19. Putting on her gloves she walked out the door.

20. Closing the book, she turned the light off and fell asleep.

The pairs of sentences below are each combined by changing one sentence to a participial phrase. Fill in the missing word or words which correctly complete the combined sentence.

21. The students became restless. They were bored by the long report.

    The students became restless, _____ by the long report.

22. Steve changed his mind. He ran back to the store.

    _____ his mind, Steve ran back to the store.

23. The car was painted bright orange. It was hard to miss.

    _____ bright orange, the car was hard to miss.

24. Charles dribbled the basketball with one hand. He held his bike with the other.

    _____ the basketball with one hand, Charles held his bike with the other.

25. Helen sang "Moon River." Helen was accompanied by a full orchestra.

    _____ by a full orchestra, Helen sang "Moon River."

26. Marcia packed her suitcase. She moved out of the house.

    _____ her suitcase, Marcia moved out of the house.

27. The tree was struck by lightning. It burst into flame.

    _____ by lightning, the tree burst into flame.

28. We stood under a tree. We waited for the rain to stop.

    We were standing under a tree _____ for the rain to stop.

29. The boy was frightened. He wrapped his arms around the horse's neck.

    _____, the boy wrapped his arms around the horse's neck.

30. He leaned back in his chair. He put his feet up on the desk.

_____ back in his chair, he put his feet up on the desk.

Complete the sentences below by adding a participial phrase.

31. _____, Gail ripped the knee of her jeans.

32. Paulo stormed out of the room _____ .

33. I noticed two joggers _____ .

34. _____, Steve tried to hail a cab.

35. _____, Peter was unable to start the meeting.

36. He tripped and fell on the steps _____ .

37. _____, she drove too fast and received a ticket.

38. _____, he was almost at the finish line.

39. They broke into the store _____ .

40. _____, Nancy rested by the stream.

41. _____, he began to write his report.

42. _____, the book was an overnight success.

43. He noticed three pigeons _____ .

44. _____, we almost lost our voices at the game.

45. _____, the actress had trouble finding work.

PARAGRAPH DEVELOPMENT

13. Topic Sentences and Supporting Detail

Just as a written word does not have much meaning unless it is part of a sentence, a written sentence does not have much meaning unless it is part of a paragraph. A paragraph is a series of sentences about one topic. A paragraph can have as few as three sentences, or it can have many more. Most paragraphs are between fifty and two hundred words long.

The first thing to do when writing a paragraph is to choose a topic. Many beginning writers choose topics that are too broad or general to be covered in one paragraph. Limit your topic to make it as specific as possible.

> EXAMPLE: *dogs* — much too general
> *seeing eye dogs* — still too general
> *the first seeing eye dog* — good

Most paragraphs include one sentence that tells what the topic is. The topic sentence is usually the first sentence in the paragraph. Experienced writers can write good paragraphs without a topic sentence or can put the topic sentence in the middle or at the end. Beginners should first learn to write paragraphs that start with a good topic sentence.

A topic sentence should not simply name the general topic of the paragraph. Do not write sentences like: "This paragraph is going to be about violence on television" or "I am going to write about my little brother."

Write a topic sentence that will limit your topic (make it more specific) and, usually, express an opinion about it: "Small children should not watch violent TV shows" or "My little brother's annoying habits drive me crazy."

Fill in the blank with the word that best completes the sentence.

1. A sentence provides the context for a word. A _____ provides the context for a sentence.

2. A paragraph is a series of _____ about one topic.

3. Most paragraphs are less than fifty words long.

    _____   (A) true
    _____   (B) false

4. Many beginning writers make the mistake of choosing paragraph topics that are too:

    _____   (A) general
    _____   (B) specific
    _____   (C) detailed

5. The sentence that tells the main idea of the paragraph is called the _____ sentence.

6. All paragraphs begin with a topic sentence.

    _____   (A) true
    _____   (B) false

7. Unless you are an experienced writer, you should put your topic sentence at the _____ of the paragraph.

    _____   (A) beginning
    _____   (B) middle
    _____   (C) end

8. Which topic sentence is better?

    _____   (A) The topic of this paragraph is basketball.
    _____   (B) Basketball is my favorite sport.

Check the letter of the most specific topic.

9.   _____   (A) my little brother
      _____   (B) my little brother's annoying habits
      _____   (C) my family

10. _____   (A) The Battle of Gettysburg
      _____   (B) American History
      _____   (C) The Civil War

11. _____   (A) my favorite sports
      _____   (B) the first time I tried to ski
      _____   (C) soccer

12. _____   (A) illegal drugs
      _____   (B) drug addiction
      _____   (C) effects of cocaine use

13. _____ (A) the Civil War and its results
    _____ (B) the main reason the Civil War started
    _____ (C) three reasons why the Civil War started

14. _____ (A) the easiest constellations to identify
    _____ (B) astronomy
    _____ (C) physical science

In the blank, write G if the sentence below would make a good topic sentence, B if it would make a bad topic sentence.

15. The topic of this essay is basketball.   _____

16. My grandmother had a difficult childhood.   _____

17. This report is about China.   _____

18. Cooking with oil can be a dangerous undertaking.   _____

19. If you enjoy arts and crafts, then take a walk outside; nature provides hundreds
    of items that can be turned into lovely gifts.   _____

20. I am going to tell you about my dog, Bear.   _____

Check the letter of the best topic sentence.

21. _____ (A) The subject I picked to write about is the Great Wall of China.
    _____ (B) The Great Wall of China is the longest man-made structure in the world.
    _____ (C) China is an interesting country.

22. _____ (A) I am going to describe our school cafeteria.
    _____ (B) The way our school cafeteria looks after lunch is what this paragraph is
            about.
    _____ (C) The school cafeteria after lunch is a disgusting sight.

23. _____ (A) I don't like cooking with oil.
    _____ (B) Cooking with oil can cause accidents and injuries if people are not careful.
    _____ (C) Let me tell you what happens when you cook with oil.

24. _____ (A) Why do I like to draw?
    _____ (B) I'm going to talk about reasons why people should draw.
    _____ (C) Drawing allows a person to look at the world with entirely new eyes.

25. _____ (A) Country dancing includes many types of quadrilles, or square dances.
    _____ (B) I like to go country-dancing.
    _____ (C) I have decided to write about country dancing.

26. _____ (A) We're supposed to describe our favorite pet.
    _____ (B) Our dog's name, Bear, is quite fitting, since he looks just like one.
    _____ (C) I want to write about my family's dog.

SUPPORTING DETAIL

After writing a topic sentence, develop the paragraph by adding supporting details. Supporting details are specific reasons, examples, facts, or descriptions that back up the topic sentence.

Many beginning writers do not develop a paragraph with supporting details. Instead, they make the mistake of simply restating the topic sentence over and over, as in the example below.

The school cafeteria after lunch is a disgusting sight. It really looks awful. The cafeteria is such a mess. After people are done eating, the cafeteria is not cleaned up properly. Something should be done about the appearance of our school cafeteria.

Check the letter of the correct answer.

27. It is a good idea to restate the topic sentence several times in a paragraph.

    _____ (A) true
    _____ (B) false

28. A paragraph is developed correctly when supporting details are added to back up the topic sentence.

    _____ (A) true
    _____ (B) false

One of the sentences below could be used as the topic sentence, the other as a supporting detail. Check the letter of the detail.

29. _____ (A) The Great Wall of China is the largest man-made structure in the world.
    _____ (B) Astronauts orbiting the earth can see the Great Wall of China.

30. _____ (A) Hurricane Gloria caused a great deal of destruction in our city.
    _____ (B) Hundreds of beautiful, old trees were knocked down by the strong winds.

31. _____ (A) Low-salt food products are becoming very popular.
    _____ (B) People nowadays are becoming very aware of the food they eat.

32. _____ (A) Michael's bedroom is always a mess.
    _____ (B) Dirty clothes lie in damp mounds on the floor.

33. _____ (A) Items of such delicate fabric should never be put into a dryer.
    _____ (B) Clothing made out of silk requires very special care.

Check the letter of the topic sentence from each set of related sentences.

34. _____ (A) A "one-horse" town is very small.
    _____ (B) A person who is "two-faced" is hypocritical.
    _____ (C) Many figures of speech use numbers.
    _____ (D) Prisoners may be given the "third degree."
    _____ (E) It's not a compliment to be called a "four-flusher."

35. _____ (A) Begin by cutting meat into one-inch cubes.
    _____ (B) Next, shake the cubes in a bag with a bit of flour.
    _____ (C) Brown the floured cubes of meat in hot fat.
    _____ (D) After the meat has browned, add water to cover.
    _____ (E) Making beef stew is not difficult.

36. _____ (A) My cousin Ralph is my least favorite relative.
    _____ (B) Ralph makes fun of me because I'm short.
    _____ (C) Ralph sneaks into my room and reads my diary.
    _____ (D) Ralph has repulsive table manners.
    _____ (E) Ralph teases my dog.

37. _____ (A) John Denver's real name is Henry John Deutschendorf, Jr.
    _____ (B) Many Hollywood stars changed their original names.
    _____ (C) John Wayne's parents named him Marion Morrison.
    _____ (D) Cary Grant's original name is Archibald Leach.

38. _____ (A) It is also too expensive to outfit both boys' and girls' football teams.
    _____ (B) Some teachers still believe that football is too rough a game for girls to play.
    _____ (C) There are several reasons why my school still does not allow girls to play football.
    _____ (D) The school board believes that girls' teams should have women coaches, and our school does not have a woman teacher who wants to coach girls' football.
    _____ (E) None of the other schools in our area have girls' football teams, so we would have no one to play against.

39. _____ (A) The film boasted an all-star cast.
    _____ (B) The special effects were gripping and original.
    _____ (C) It was directed by a man who had won three Oscars.
    _____ (D) The movie studio that produced the film could not understand why the film had not been well-received by the public.
    _____ (E) Many of the scenes had been filmed in the stunning Australian wilderness.

In the blank provided, indicate whether the following paragraphs:

(A) have been developed with specific ideas.
(B) have not been developed properly and keep restating the topic sentence.

40.

After lunch, our school cafeteria is a disgusting sight. Abandoned trays with half-eaten hamburgers and soggy French fries litter the tables. Puddles of milk slowly drip onto the floor, joining the crumpled milk cartons and wads of napkins. Students should be required to clean up after themselves.

_____

41.

The Great Wall of China is the longest man-made structure in the world. Throughout history, nothing longer than the Great Wall of China has ever been built. Because of its great size, the Great Wall of China is truly an impressive sight.

_____

42.

My little brother's eating habits make me sick. At breakfast he fills his cereal bowl with milk and stirs and stirs until the Cheerios turn to mush. At lunch he dismantles his sandwich and eats only the bread. At dinner he carefully spreads out the mashed potatoes until they cover his entire plate.

_____

43.

My little brother's eating habits drive me crazy. The way he eats his breakfast is really disgusting. At lunchtime he does horrible things with his food. I can hardly stand to watch him eat.

_____

44.

The Great Wall of China is the longest man-made structure in the world. The main section of the wall is approximately 2,150 miles long. Several additional sections add another 1,800 miles, making the entire wall nearly 4,000 miles in length. The Great Wall is so large that astronauts are able to see it while orbiting the earth.

_____

45.

Soccer is a better sport than football. I prefer soccer to football and so do many of my friends. Football is just not as good a game as soccer. If you try both sports, I think you will like soccer better, too!

_____

14. Paragraph Unity

A well-written paragraph has unity. All the specific details used to develop the paragraph must fit the topic expressed in the topic sentence.

Check the letter of the general topic. Then put an X by the letter of the one specific detail that does NOT belong.

1. _____ (A) water skiing
   _____ (B) baseball
   _____ (C) soccer
   _____ (D) basketball
   _____ (E) team sports

2. _____ (A) motor vehicles
   _____ (B) automobiles
   _____ (C) bicycles
   _____ (D) trucks
   _____ (E) motorboats

3. _____ (A) social studies
   _____ (B) mathematics
   _____ (C) school subjects
   _____ (D) our cafeteria
   _____ (E) earth science

4. _____ (A) Sweden
   _____ (B) France
   _____ (C) countries
   _____ (D) Canada
   _____ (E) Asia

5. _____ (A) the death of her father when Mother was two
   _____ (B) Mother's blond hair and blue eyes
   _____ (C) the family's poverty during Mother's childhood
   _____ (D) Mother's difficult childhood
   _____ (E) Mother's frequent illness as a little girl

6. _____ (A) chicken fried rice
   _____ (B) spagetti and meatballs
   _____ (C) egg rolls
   _____ (D) Chinese food
   _____ (E) sweet and sour pork

Check the letter of the topic sentence. Then put an X by the letter of the detail that does not fit.

7. _____ (A) The Great Wall of China is an impressive sight.
   _____ (B) Its four thousand-mile length makes it the longest man-made structure in the world.
   _____ (C) The Great Wall is about twenty-five feet high and fifteen feet wide.
   _____ (D) The Great Wall was built to protect the Chinese border.
   _____ (E) Forty-foot watchtowers line the wall.

8. _____ (A) There are fewer serious injuries in basketball games.
   _____ (B) Girls can play basketball, but most schools will not allow them to play football.
   _____ (C) Basketball is a better game for schools than football.
   _____ (D) Professional football players earn a great deal of money.
   _____ (E) Basketball uniforms are less expensive than football uniforms.

9. _____ (A) Michael abandons his sneakers on the kitchen floor.
   _____ (B) His wastebasket overflows onto the floor.
   _____ (C) Michael's room is carpeted with piles of clothing.
   _____ (D) Michael's room is a hopeless mess.
   _____ (E) Dirty plates and glasses from a dozen snacks line his dresser.

10. _____ (A) The number three is significant in many stories.
    _____ (B) Characters are given three wishes, not two or four.
    _____ (C) Think of "The Three Little Pigs" or "Goldilocks and the Three Bears."
    _____ (D) The number seven is also important.

In the blank, write the number of the sentence(s) that does not belong. If all the details support the topic sentence, write OK.

11.

   (1) Noise pollution is a growing problem in the modern world. (2) Radios blare on crowded beaches. (3) Many factories are so noisy that workers must wear earplugs to protect their hearing. (4) Factories are often hot and uncomfortable places to work. (5) People whose houses are near large airports must live with the continual roar of the jets.

   _____

12.

   (1) The ancient Egyptians worshipped cats. (2) An Egyptian goddess of love named Bast had the head of a cat and the body of a woman. (3) Egyptians were punished by death for killing cats. (4) Thousands of dead cats were reverently made into mummies and buried in special cat cemeteries.

   _____

13.

(1) Hurricane Gloria caused a great deal of damage. (2) Many beautiful old trees were destroyed. (3) Power lines were torn down by the wind. (4) Houses near the water were flooded by huge waves. (5) The hurricane was covered thoroughly by the news media.

_____

14.

(1) Left-handed people have many difficulties in this society. (2) Many left-handed children have a hard time learning how to write neatly because they must write across the page from left to right, causing the letters to smudge. (3) Some languages, like Arabic and Hebrew, are written from right to left. (4) Many right-handed tools, such as scissors, are hard for left-handed people to use.

_____

15.

(1) Thousands of years ago in Ancient Greece there lived a girl named Arachne. (2) Arachne was very proud and arrogant. (3) She was also an expert weaver among mortals. (4) She used a wooden loom. (5) She was so good that one day she challenged the goddess Athena to a weaving contest, believing that she could easily win. (6) On the day of the contest, Arachne wove a tapestry that was indeed beautiful, but it showed the gods and goddesses making fools of themselves. (7) The tapestry was almost five feet high and six feet wide. (8) Arachne's lack of respect for the gods made Athena so angry that she changed Arachne into a spider and commanded her to weave for the rest of her life.

_____

16.

(1) The mayor-council plan is the oldest form of city government in the United States. (2) Under this plan, voters elect a mayor and a lawmaking council. (3) They are elected by all of the voters in a city, or by only those voters in their sections of the city. (4) In the mayor-council plan of city government, the council makes the laws and the mayor enforces them. (5) The borough of West Chester, Pennsylvania, runs under a mayor-council plan.

_____

15. Paragraph Purpose

Writing is often classified according to its purpose. A paragraph can be descriptive: its purpose is to tell the reader how something looks, sounds, feels, or tastes. A paragraph can be narrative: its purpose is to tell a story. When people talk about "creative" writing, they usually mean description or narration.

Expository writing is another category. Expository means explanatory. The purpose of expository writing is to present and explain facts, ideas, and opinions. Reports and essays are examples of expository writing. Most writing done in schools and businesses is expository.

Another way of classifying writing is into fiction or nonfiction. Fiction is "made up." A work of fiction can be based on things that really happened, but it includes imaginary events and characters. It does not have to be "true." Expository writing is always nonfiction; "creative" writing usually refers to fiction.

Check the letter which provides the best answer.

1. Narration means:

    _____ (A) describing a scene
    _____ (B) telling a story
    _____ (C) comparing two things

2. Descriptive and narrative writing are often referred to as _____ writing.

3. Which of these are you likely to write in a creative writing class? (More than one may be right.)

    _____ (A) a book report
    _____ (B) a poem
    _____ (C) a short story
    _____ (D) a paragraph explaining photosynthesis
    _____ (E) a description of a sunset

4. Expository means:

    _____ (A) creative
    _____ (B) unified
    _____ (C) explanatory
    _____ (D) fictional

5a. Which of the following are examples of expository writing?

        _____   (A) a magazine article
        _____   (B) a poem
        _____   (C) an essay explaining your views on war
        _____   (D) the book, THE WIZARD OF OZ

5b. _____   (A) Poe's poem "The Raven"
        _____   (B) a book report
        _____   (C) a short story
        _____   (D) a newspaper article
        _____   (E) a paragraph explaining your opinion on drunken driving

6. To say that something is "fiction" means that it is factual.

        _____   (A) true
        _____   (B) false

Indicate whether the following paragraphs are examples of:

    (A) descriptive writing
    (B) narrative writing
    (C) expository writing

7.

    The ancient Egyptians worshipped cats. An Egyptian goddess of love named Bast had the head of a cat and the body of a woman. Egyptians were punished by death for killing cats. Dead cats were made into mummies and carefully buried in cat cemeteries.

        _____

8.

    Once upon a time in ancient Greece there lived a girl named Arachne. She was such an expert weaver that she challenged the goddess Athena to a weaving contest. After the contest, which Arachne won, Athena became so angry that she changed the girl into a spider.

        _____

9.

    Michael's room is a hopeless mess. The entire floor is carpeted with piles of clothes, both dirty and clean. Plates and glasses from a dozen snacks line his dresser. Michael's bed has not been made since it entered his room.

        _____

Indicate whether the written works below are:

(A) *fiction*
(B) *nonfiction*

10. Poe's poem "The Raven"   _____

11. a newspaper article on an election   _____

12. a report on the Civil War   _____

13. "The Three Little Pigs"   _____

14. a paragraph comparing golf and tennis   _____

16. the book THE WIZARD OF OZ   _____

17. directions on how to assemble a lawnmower   _____

18. the film "Star Wars"   _____

19. a recipe for gingerbread   _____

20. a description of the Oregon Trail   _____

16. Paragraph Coherence

In order to know how to organize the details in a paragraph, you must know what the purpose of the paragraph is to be. Narrative paragraphs and those which give step-by-step instructions are the easiest to organize. Just put the details in the order in which they happen. This "time" order is called chronological order.

A well-organized paragraph that moves smoothly from one sentence to another is a coherent paragraph. "Coherent" means "hanging together." A good way to move from one sentence to the next in a chronological paragraph is to start sentences with words and phrases that show "time" order.

Words and phrases used to connect details and show how they are related in a paragraph are often called transition words. Examples of chronological transition words are: *first, then, next, soon, afterward*, and *finally*.

Check the letter that provides the correct answer.

1. "Chronological" comes from the Greek root "chronos," which means

   _____ (A) detail.
   _____ (B) time.
   _____ (C) writing.

2. A transition word is one that

   _____ (A) introduces a topic.
   _____ (B) helps the reader move from one idea to another.
   _____ (C) is repeated frequently or ends a paragraph.

3. *After moving from Los Angeles to New York, Charles found it difficult to make the transition to his new home.* In this sentence, the word "transition" probably means

   _____ (A) hanging together.
   _____ (B) passage from one thing to another.
   _____ (C) organization.

4. Which set of transition words and phrases would be good in a narrative paragraph?

   _____ (A) moreover, however, on the other hand
   _____ (B) to the left, straight ahead, under the table
   _____ (C) first, then, next, finally

5. Chronological transition words are those which

   _____ (A) describe the location of objects.
   _____ (B) describe how to organize a topic sentence.
   _____ (C) describe the order in which something was done or something happened.

Check the kinds of paragraph(s) you think should be organized chronologically.

6. _____ (A) a story
   _____ (B) a description
   _____ (C) step-by-step directions
   _____ (D) a comparison of two things
   _____ (E) a report on the Civil War
   _____ (F) a comparison of soccer and football
   _____ (G) directions on how to get to school from your house
   _____ (H) a list of all the things that went wrong today
   _____ (I) a description of your room
   _____ (J) a recipe for strawberry shortcake

Check the letter of the word or phrase that shows chronological order.

7. _____ (A) because
   _____ (B) first
   _____ (C) moreover

8. _____ (A) next
   _____ (B) nevertheless
   _____ (C) since

9. _____ (A) in the morning
   _____ (B) however
   _____ (C) on the other hand

10. _____ (A) moreover
    _____ (B) later
    _____ (C) in addition

11. _____ (A) meanwhile
    _____ (B) in order to
    _____ (C) due to the fact that

12. _____ (A) so that
    _____ (B) furthermore
    _____ (C) while

In each of the questions below, number the letters in chronological order.

13. _____ (A) Both the car and the truck burst into flames.
    _____ (B) He was rushed to the hospital.
    _____ (C) A terrible accident happened on Shore Drive yesterday.
    _____ (D) The truck driver was badly injured.
    _____ (E) Luckily, no one else was injured.
    _____ (F) A gasoline truck crashed into an abandoned car.

14. _____ (A) Here is one way to make a grilled cheese sandwich.
    _____ (B) Put a slice of cheese on the slice of bread in the pan.
    _____ (C) Butter two slices of bread.
    _____ (D) Flip the sandwich over and fry the other side.
    _____ (E) Place one slice, buttered side down, in a hot pan.
    _____ (F) Put the second slice of bread, buttered side up, on the cheese.

15. _____ (A) Martha decided to sell the length of hair to a dollmaker.
    _____ (B) Martha had waist-length hair.
    _____ (C) The dollmaker paid Martha $85.00.
    _____ (D) The hairdresser cut off a two-foot length of hair.
    _____ (E) She decided to have it cut very short.

16. _____ (A) At breakfast, the baby poured an entire box of cereal on the floor.
    _____ (B) First, I overslept.
    _____ (C) Then he cried for the rest of the morning.
    _____ (D) When I tried to take a shower before breakfast, the hot water was all gone.

17. _____ (A) She first went to the library to return the books she had borrowed.
    _____ (B) After visiting with her sister, Joanne went to art class.
    _____ (C) From the library she went to the market to buy some fruit and flowers.
    _____ (D) Joanne had several errands to run today.
    _____ (E) When class was over, she went home to write some letters.
    _____ (F) She then went to deliver the fruit and flowers to her sister in the hospital.

Read the following paragraph. Decide which transition words you would use in the blanks. Then in the list below, check the word or words that you think would fit into at least one of the blanks in the paragraph.

Here is one way to make a grilled cheese sandwich. (1) _____, butter two slices of bread. (2) _____ place one slice, buttered side down, in a hot pan. Put a slice of cheese on the bread in the pan. Now put the second slice of bread, buttered side up, on the cheese. (3) _____, flip the sandwich over and fry the other side.

18. _____ (A) Then
    _____ (B) First
    _____ (C) However
    _____ (D) Next
    _____ (E) Second
    _____ (F) Then
    _____ (G) Before this
    _____ (H) Next
    _____ (I) Third
    _____ (J) Lastly
    _____ (K) However
    _____ (L) Finally

ORGANIZATION IN DESCRIPTIVE PARAGRAPHS

When writing a descriptive paragraph, you should also organize the details according to a plan. Make the location of the details clear enough so that the reader can "see" how each one fits into the picture. Instead of using chronological order, put the details in spatial order or in order of location: from top to bottom, left to right, or nearest to farthest.

Words that show location are often prepositions such as "behind," "next to," "beside," "between," "under," and "above." A preposition is used as part of a phrase ending with a noun or pronoun.

EXAMPLES: under the table
                      behind him

Check the letter of the answer which best completes the sentence.

19.   A description should be written in chronological order.

_____   (A) true
_____   (B) false

20. "Spatial" has to do with

_____   (A) time.
_____   (B) order.
_____   (C) space.

21. "Spatial order" means the same as

_____   (A) chronological order.
_____   (B) order of location.
_____   (C) order of importance.

22. Prepositional phrases often provide transitions in descriptive paragraphs by describing

_____   (A) degree of importance.
_____   (B) length of time.
_____   (C) location.

23. Which of the sentences below begins with a prepositional phrase?
_____   (A) On the trees were the last crisp, orange leaves of autumn.
_____   (B) If we forget to invite Sam, he'll be terribly angry.
_____   (C) Silently the snowflakes fell.